DOMINIQUE'S STRANGE NEW WORLD

The Adventures of a Retired Racing Greyhound

To EMMA,
THE CUTEST GODDAUGHTER
EVER!
♡

ENJOY,

Diane Casenta Galutia
7-4-16

WRITTEN BY
DIANE CASENTA GALUTIA

Illustrated by Gabriel C.Tumblod

PAGE PUBLISHING, INC.
New York, NY

First originally published by Page Publishing, Inc. 2015

ISBN 978-1-68139-307-0 (pbk)
ISBN 978-1-68139-308-7 (digital)

Printed in the United States of America

DEDICATION

This book is dedicated first and foremost to our amazing and loving greyhounds, Dominique and Cokie, as well as our incredibly funny and cuddly Italian greyhounds, John Boy and Bambi. They were the inspiration for writing this book. A special dedication also goes out to all the greyhound adoption groups, rescue and adoption groups for all animals, and the selfless volunteers throughout the globe who work tirelessly to save so many lives.

ACKNOWLEDGEMENTS

I wish to thank God for all the blessings in my life and for this opportunity to share my story. I also want to thank my incredible husband, Dave, for his continued support and faith in me that I can do anything I set out to do. I am also very grateful to my family members and friends for all of their encouragement. A special thank you to Peggy and Lew Levin of Personalized Greyhounds of Central Pennsylvania from whom we adopted our beloved greyhounds, Dominique and Cokie.

CHAPTER 1

"Come on, Dominique! You're almost there, girl!"

"Come on, number three!"

As the hot Arizona sun blazed in the sky, I could feel the heat through my red racing silk and my temples throbbing. My heart was beating so loud that I almost couldn't hear the roar of the crowd as they stood and cheered when I took the lead.

I was almost there…the home stretch. Then, a loud *pop*! I could barely stand the pain as I began to hobble. I collapsed just short of the finish line, and all the other dogs sped by me.

Suddenly the cheers turned to boos as many walked away shaking their heads. I could only guess how many had placed their bets on me to win. You see, up until that point, I was a champion racer and the star of the show. Many assumed I would be headed for the greyhound racing Hall of Fame, just as my paw, grandpaw, and great-grandpaw before me. In our world, there is no greater honor than that. I never played with other dogs when I was a puppy. All I remember is training hard every day. Then when I was ready to race, they loaded me into a truck and took me far away to a track in Arizona. My whole focus was on winning. I knew winning was everything and that my worth came from crossing that finish line first.

However, sometimes things don't turn out as we plan, as I would soon learn. Yes. My hip eventually healed, and the pain subsided, but I would never again be fast enough to compete. The humans decided I would have to leave the track so they could make room for other, faster dogs.

That injury ended my racing career, and I was facing a whole new strange world, a world of a retired racing greyhound. What do greyhounds do in retirement? Racing was all I had ever known. Day after day for more than four years I was either training to run or competing to win. I could feel my stomach churning as I anticipated a future without racing. Oh, what would I do!

CHAPTER 2

Meanwhile, back in a small East Coast town, Maria was about to celebrate her ninth birthday. Her parents always said she could have her own puppy once she was old enough to appreciate the responsibility of caring for a pet. She knew this was finally the year. Maria could hardly sleep as she tossed and turned, thinking about her birthday tomorrow and anticipating her surprise when she sees her new cuddly puppy.

"I wonder what kind of puppy Mom and Dad are buying for me. Will it have long or short hair? Will it be black, white, brown, or even spotted? I'll bet it'll have a pretty bow around its neck."

After what seemed like the longest night ever, the big day finally arrived. Maria was giddy with anticipation as she sat at the breakfast table. She wondered where her puppy was hiding.

Then something odd happened. Her parents brought her a small box and told her to unwrap it. Her face sank as she began to realize she wouldn't be getting her dog this year. After all, the box was way too small to fit a puppy. Holding back the tears, Maria slowly opened the little box. Inside was a piece of folded paper.

Maria's mom said, "Go ahead, honey. Open the paper and read what's on it."

"I really wanted a puppy this year, and I thought for sure…"

"Please, dear, read the letter, and you'll understand why we didn't get you a puppy."

"Sure, Mom."

Maria unfolded the letter and started reading aloud. "Dear Maria, as you're now ready to appreciate having a dog to care for, your very own retired racing greyhound is waiting for you to bring her into our home and your heart. Love, Mom and Dad."

Maria welled up with tears and ran to hug her parents.

CHAPTER 3

The next thing I knew, I was loaded into a big van with five others who also let the humans down by not running fast enough. We rode for what seemed like forever. Where were we headed? I could hear my heart pound—*poom, poom, poom*—as we traveled down the long bumpy driveway. Then the driver, who was singing to the radio for most of the trip, finally turned off the music and spoke. "Well, gang. Here we are. This is your new temporary quarters. The folks you're going to meet work on finding forever homes for retired greyhounds. They'll take good care of you until you're adopted."

The man proceeded to unload us one by one from the van and walked us through the basement door of the house. A woman with a gentle smile promptly greeted us. I was the last one through the door. Then our driver gave us each a quick pat on the back, wished us well, and vanished.

The woman walked by and inspected each of us. When she approached me, she stopped, shook her head, and said, "My, my. I think you'll go first. I'll bet you're white under all that dirt and dust. I see that part of your racing name was Dominique. What you need, Dominique, is a good scrubbing. I know you'll want to look your best when your new family comes to meet you." The woman's young helper opened the door of my crate and guided me into a big shower and shampooed me from head to tail. How refreshing to finally have a good bath! I watched in amazement as the clear water turned brown and then gradually clear again as the grime rolled off my back. The warm dryer afterward felt good, yet I couldn't stop my teeth from chattering. Would my new humans accept me, even though I could no longer run as fast? Or would they reject me as others had done when I stopped winning? Could I please these strangers?

One by one my buddies said good-bye and wished me luck as they left with their new humans. The next morning after breakfast, the kind woman smiled and told me I was about to meet my new family.

Later that morning, I heard the crunching of tires on the long driveway. A young girl rushed through the door, and our eyes met. Maria's parents came in right behind her. "Maria," whispered her mom, "This has to be the one that's going to be your new dog. She's even more beautiful than the way she was described over the phone."

Full of tears, Maria knelt before me and cuddled me ever so tenderly. "Hello, girl. We're finally here to take you home."

The woman who lived in the house said, "Her racing name was Dominique. You can feel free to change it if you'd like."

Maria said, "I love her name. She looks like a Dominique. Besides, I'm sure she's used to that name by now, so it wouldn't be fair to change it on her. Right, Dominique?"

Before we were sent on our way, I listened carefully while my new family was given lots of information on the special needs of a retired racing greyhound. They were told, "During their racing careers, greyhounds aren't exposed to the simple household items other dogs take for granted. Be especially careful of Dominique around any glass door, as she may not realize it's made of solid glass and will attempt to walk right through. And don't expect her to know how to climb stairs. Most likely, she's never seen a set of stairs. She must be introduced slowly to her new environment, just as a young child. Another thing to keep in mind is that she has spent her entire life surrounded by greyhounds and probably hasn't been around other dogs. She knows only her own kind, and other breeds might make her uncomfortable at first."

As I lay by Maria's side, I realized I would have much to learn about this strange new life outside the track.

CHAPTER 4

As we entered the living room of Maria's home, a big crate with fluffy bedding awaited me. This was much nicer than the shredded paper I had to lay on at the racetrack. I could get used to this!

Maria's dad said this temporary quarters would have to do until I learned to climb stairs. He said to Maria, "Honey, remember what the lady said earlier today? She said that Dominique, like other racing greyhounds, has probably never had to climb stairs before. We'll have to teach her."

The next day, poor Maria and her dad tried their best to coax me up the stairs. They begged, pleaded, and bribed. Even as I salivated at the beefy treat they dangled above the bottom step, I gazed at the steep incline, and my legs locked. It was no use. In my heart I wanted more than anything to climb those stairs so I could sleep with Maria every night. But my fear kept me downstairs in the living room with Maria's dad sleeping on the floor next to my crate. Each day as dusk approached, I sadly anticipated Maria climbing those stairs and disappearing until the next morning.

A week went by, but it seemed like an eternity. Then one day Maria came rushing through the front door and flew up the stairs to the bathroom. I knew something was terribly wrong when she didn't stop to greet me with her usual big hug. I sprang up on all fours and raced up behind her. As Maria hung her head over the toilet, I watched in horror as all her food spilled out. Once she settled down and I knew she was okay, I realized something amazing. I was so worried about Maria that I forgot my fear of steps and was suddenly no longer downstairs! From that moment on, I ran up and down that staircase with ease, sometimes skipping steps along the way, sometimes transporting various items in my mouth. The best reward for me was that I could now sleep upstairs every night by Maria's bedside.

While exploring my new upstairs world one day, I discovered a secret room full of the best-tasting toys in every color! You see, I never had any toys to play with at the track, and these were really inviting! Some were leather with pointy little toes, some were made of canvas, and two of them were sort of furry. Later I learned they're called slipper toys. After I had done a good job chewing some of the leather ones, I proudly carried one of these treasures to Maria's mom and deposited it at her feet.

"Oh, no…Dominique! You destroyed my favorite dress shoes!"

After that, the door to the secret room was no longer open. I guess I would have to find other toys to play with.

CHAPTER 5

Life was better than ever and I was settling nicely into my new world—then it happened. Every evening, Maria and either her mom or dad would proudly walk me around the neighborhood. Passersby always *oohed* and *aahed* and asked to pet me. I would brush up against them and lick their hands in delight. Then out of the blue this strange-looking creature at the end of a leash came toward us. Greyhounds were all I had ever known, so I tried to keep my distance. Then, that little bully ran right up and bit me in the side.

"Ouch! That hurt," I cried.

Maria's mom reacted quickly and stood between us to protect me from any more abuse. Thankfully, my delicate paper-thin skin hadn't been badly punctured. Once we arrived home, Maria's mom fixed me up and told me how sorry she was that she didn't prevent this little dog from biting me. I thought, "Maybe greyhounds are the only friendly dogs."

My perception of other kinds of dogs would soon change. It was time for my first sleepover. After being in my new home for a few months, Maria and her parents were going away for a couple of days, and they packed up my bed and dropped me off to stay with another family. When I arrived, three lazy greyhounds were sprawled out in front of the fireplace. They all managed to look up, yawn, raise an eyebrow, and continue their naps. Then I met their leader…a little bit of a dog. At first I backed up because I expected him to bite me as the little bully in my neighborhood had done. I was surprised when this little furry guy approached me, wagged his tail, and told me his name was Louie. We chatted a while, and I told him about my life on the track and how my new family adopted me. Louie then asked me to follow him. He led me on a tour of his house.

"Since you're so new to this life of retirement, Dominique, you probably have never seen yourself in a mirror. You're a beautiful girl."

Louie escorted me down the hall to my very first mirror. He stayed in the background as I stood in front of that full-length glass and marveled at my sleek muscular body. My years of racing had kept me very fit. And I must say, my bright red collar with fancy blue-and-gold trim looked majestic against my silky white fur and carefully placed black spots. Louie said I looked just like an elegant version of a Dalmatian that had been dieting.

Louie also introduced me to a treasure chest of toys. I took every toy out of that box, dragged it across the room, and laid each one in front of me. The other lazy greyhounds watched as I joyfully tossed stuffed toys of every shape and size through the air. This was almost as much fun as the shoe toys in the secret room, the one I could no longer enter.

When Maria came running in to take me back home, I wagged my tail in delight. During that long country ride, I thought how lucky I was to have Maria and also how glad I was to meet Louie. Not only did he introduce me to that magical mirror; thanks to Louie and his warm hospitality, the next time I'd see a dog other than a greyhound, I'd try to make friends.

CHAPTER 6

As months passed, we were all settled into our routines. Life was amazing, and I was about to attend my very first picnic! My family loaded up the car, and we drove out to the country. My eyes grew in amazement as we pulled up. There on the lawn was a sea of greyhounds and their humans! Retired racing dogs of all sizes and colors were spread out on blankets everywhere. While most of the dogs had already found their forever homes, I also found out that some of the greyhounds were at the picnic with the hope of being adopted.

I was basking in the sun minding my own business when Maria's dad approached my blanket with a petite greyhound attached to the other end of a leash. He introduced her as Cokie. She proceeded to plop herself right on my blanket and almost pushed me off! Then she grabbed the plush toy from between my front paws and began squeaking it. It took everything inside me not to growl at this rude newcomer. She then batted her big brown eyes at Maria and licked her face. The next thing I knew, Maria was saying, "Oh, look! I think Cokie really likes me, and look how nice Dominique is sharing her blanket. It seems she and Cokie have really hit it off. Can we please take Cokie home? You know how we've been talking about getting another dog to keep Dominique company when we're out during the day. Please, please, Mom and Dad, can we keep her?"

Didn't Maria realize? I liked being the only dog. I didn't need a sister. I had all the love I needed. This would mean I'd have to share Maria's affections…and my toys!

It didn't seem to matter what I thought. Cokie would be joining our family. She was only two and a half and full of energy. Just as she had done at the picnic, she took over everything. She pushed me off my bed, stole my toys, ate my food, and most of all, befriended *my* family. Everyone thought she was *soooo* cute. I snubbed Cokie and everyone else…even Maria. I'd show them. Maybe if they saw how hurt and upset I was, they would return Cokie. I'm sure she came with a money-back guarantee.

While shuffling past the family room with my head hung low, I overheard Maria sobbing as she told her parents she made a big mistake bringing Cokie into their home. She confessed that she really tried to do the right thing and it ended up hurting me. Her dad agreed that maybe they should return Cokie to the adoption agency and try to find another home for her. He also said that Cokie had already been adopted once before and returned because of her bad manners. She would be tough to place a third time.

I suddenly felt sorry for poor Cokie girl. What a jerk I had been! I guess Cokie was still young and didn't really know any better. I had to go find Cokie and welcome her into our home. I pranced into the living room and found her lying all curled up on my dog bed. I told her I was sorry that I had acted so selfishly and that I really wanted her with us. She perked right up and proceeded to lick my face. My family noticed the change in my attitude and decided to keep my new sister. Don't get me wrong. Cokie still stole my toys, ate my food, pushed me out of my bed, and nuzzled my humans for attention; but somehow I no longer minded and actually grew very fond of her. Even though Cokie and I slept much of the time, I liked the company in that big lonely house whenever our family had to go out somewhere.

Cokie and I had become quite accustomed to our life together. I most enjoyed our family vacations to Maria's grandparents' beach house, where Cokie and I were actually allowed to jump up on the sofas instead of sneaking up on them at home. We'd take long walks up and down the beach. How soft the sand felt between my paws! Maria's grandfather would cook on the grill and "accidentally" drop a hamburger or two on the ground. This sure beat the boring dog food at home. What a great life with my sister Cokie and my forever family!

CHAPTER 7

Just when life really gets comfortable, everything changes. Maria's dad came home from work and announced that he had heard about two little Italian greyhounds that had just arrived at the local shelter. He said they were six years old and had already been returned by two different owners. These dogs desperately needed a forever home. The next thing I knew the family loaded us up and took us to the shelter to meet them. I was amazed when I saw how much these little dogs looked like Cokie and me; only they were shrunken down versions. We all just looked at each other, did some of the obligatory sniffing, and then went about our business. Maria's mom said, "Look Maria. They all seem to be getting along so beautifully. We just can't leave these two here. And since they're brother and sister, it wouldn't be right to separate them. We'll have to adopt both of them."

The next thing I knew, all seven of us were riding back to our house. Our two new housemates were John Boy and Bambi. These were the names they came with, and as with me, Maria didn't have the heart to change their names.

John Boy became king. Twice the size of Bambi and all of thirteen pounds, John Boy took over our beds, stole our food, and generally growled as we approached him or Bambi. Amazingly, Cokie started to back off as she realized John Boy ruled. After all this time, Cokie no longer bullied me and when I approached, she even started giving me *her* dog bed!

Little Bambi must have thought she was bigger than all of us. She would climb on top of the back of the sofa and force her way right into everyone's face and bark. It's funny how she only did that when John Boy was by her side for moral support.

How strange to see the family dynamics change with the addition of our new brother and sister! I had to admit, it was nice seeing the positive change in Cokie.

CHAPTER 8

Years have passed since that day I limped off the track and cautiously entered my for-ever home. Today as I lay all cuddled up with Cokie, John Boy, and Bambi, I can't help but reflect and smile as I finally realize my purpose in life. It doesn't matter how fast I run, or how many races I win. What matters is what's in my heart. I'm here to watch out for Cokie and to keep John Boy and Bambi out of trouble. But most of all, my role is to care for and love Maria and her parents. My racing career may have ended that day many years ago in the hot Arizona sun, but I've realized that I don't have to be the best at anything to be special. I've learned that just by giving unconditional love to others, I get so much more in return. I've also learned that this new world isn't so strange after all. In fact, I wouldn't trade it for anything.

ABOUT THE AUTHOR

Diane Casenta Galutia is a Pennsylvania native. This is her first children's book, which combines her love of animals with her passion for writing. In her professional life, she has had the opportunity to utilize her writing and editing skills in various communications roles within the healthcare, public and private sectors. She is a member of the Society of Children's Book Writers and Illustrators and has attended several of the organization's workshops.

CPSIA information can be obtained
at www.ICGtesting.com
Printed in the USA
LVOW05s1103081215
465916LV00005B/15/P